YOU CAN'T CATCH
IT HOLDING HANDS

Niki de Saint Phalle

Acknowledgments

The Publishers would like to thank the many medical experts who reviewed the entire contents of this book to make sure that the information contained herein accurately reflects the latest scientific findings on AIDS. Special thanks for their continued support and suggestions go to Dr. William Haseltine, Chief of Cancer Pharmacology, Harvard Medical School; Dr. Paul Volberding, Chief, AIDS Activities Division, University of California Medical Center; and Dr. Jordan U. Gutterman, Chairman, Department of Clinical Immunology, The University of Texas System Cancer Center.

The Lapis Press
1850 Union Street, Suite 466
San Francisco, CA 94123

ISBN 0-932499-52-X *hardcover*

I made this book together
with DR. Silvio Barandun.
We want to thank
Geoffrey Humphreys for his help.

New York April, 87

Dear PHiLiP,

Last night I had a visit from my friend Dr. BARANdun.

He is a well-known immunologist.

This is what he told me:

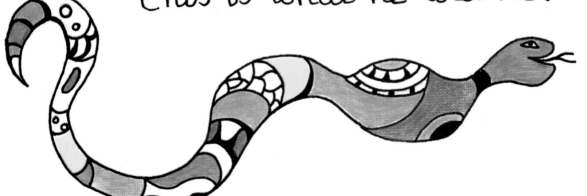

AIDS is caused by a Virus which lives mainly in BLOOD and SPERM and VAGINAL FLUIDS.

It can be found also in saliva, intestinal secretions and even in tears. It can survive outside the body as well

IN SYRINGES and NEEDLES

The AIDS VIRUS can only invade a healthy body by entering the bloodstream (through needles or by making LOVE). It does not enter the body through the outer skin.

AIDS is transmitted almost always by making **LOVE** (anal, oral or vaginal sex).

MEN CAN GIVE IT to **MEN** and **WOMEN**.

WOMEN CAN GIVE it to **MEN** and perhaps to **WOMEN**.

DRUG USERS can also transmit **AIDS** by exchanging needles.

YOU CAN'T CATCH IT FROM

a flower

A DOG

a cat

a mosquito or a fly

from a canary

YOU CAN'T CATCH it FROM

spoon

plates
food

fork

knife

glasses

10$

MONEY

combs

books

door
knobs

your hairdresser

13

To my GREAT RELIEF you can't get it from a toilet seat

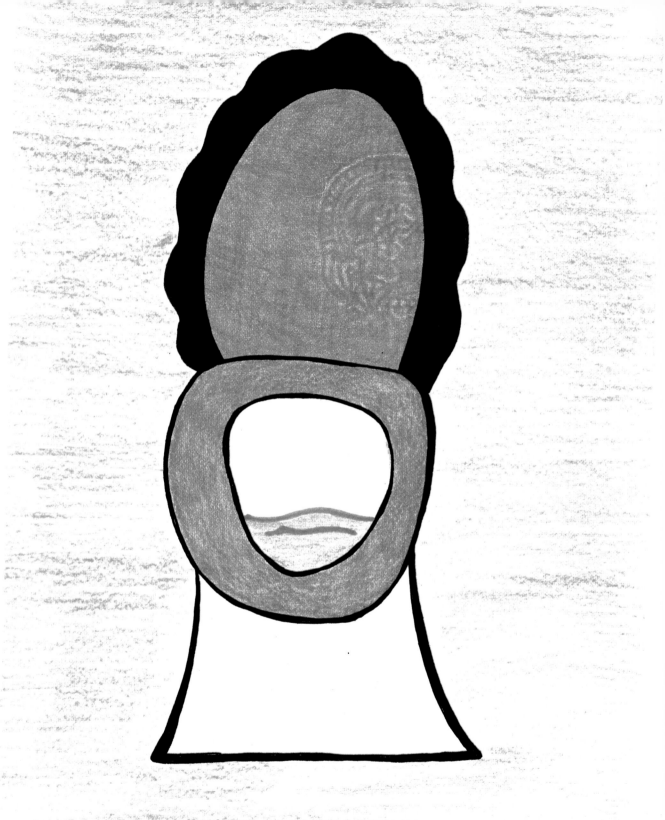

GOOD NEWS FOR NUNS AND MONKS

AND FAITHFUL COUPLES

they can't catch it

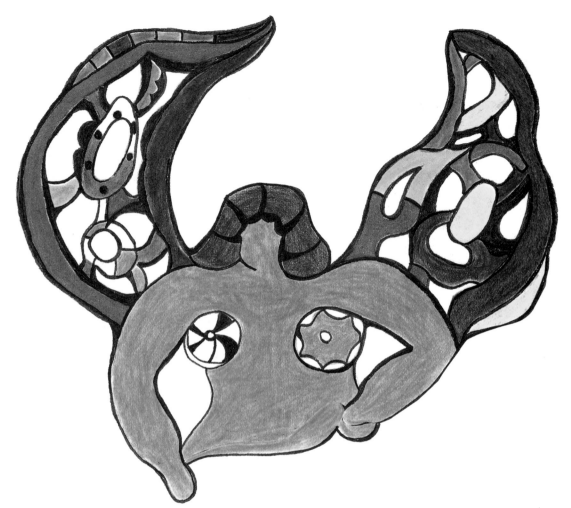

But IF yOU'RE NO
ANGEL

then take the following
precautions

KNOW the PERSON
for some time
and HIS OR HER
HABITS before
you make love.

If you don't want to take
any risk

No PASSionate
French Kissing
with strangers.

But you can touch all over

NO SEX PARTIES

21

If you are a big
ROMEO

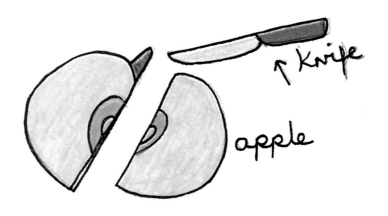

↑ Knife

apple

$$\frac{1}{2}$$

It WON'T BE ENOUGH
to cut your love life
in half.
Reduce the number of
your lovers as much as possible.

THERE IS SAFETY

IN NUMBERS

NO Numbers

1

Best one
faithful
lover

2

3

4

you can get
AIDS from one
pick up with
an infected
person

There is some safety in Rubbers

USE A RUBBER

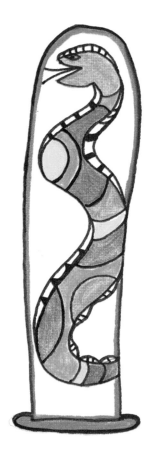

← what do you think of these?

It may not be your cup of tea but it will save lives.

Tell your GAY FRIENDS
SAFER SEX ONLY

NO SAUNAS no "bathhouse"
(they might get carried away)
AT THE DISCO
ONLY DANCE
WATCH OUT FOR PICK UPS

DRUG USERS

NEVER

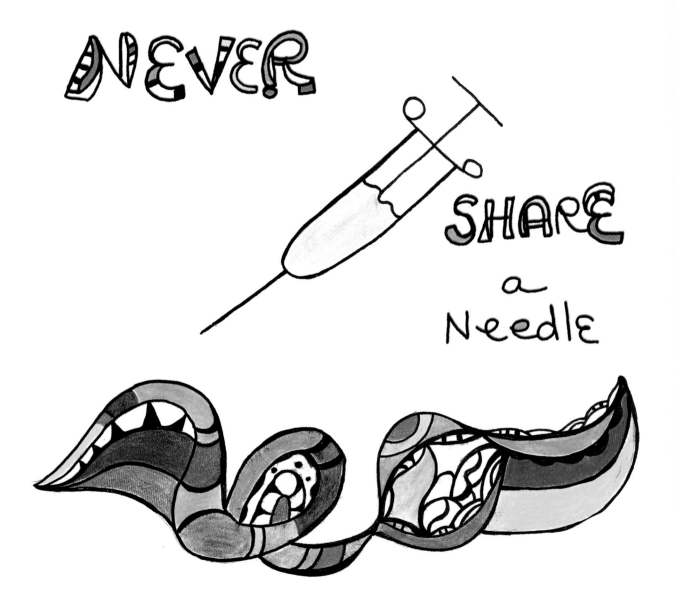

SHARE a Needle

TAKE EXTRA CARE

At the tattoo parlor

At the acupuncturist

see that everything
is sterilized.

CHILDREN
CAN

GO TO SCHOOL TOGETHER
PLAY TOGETHER
TAKE A BATH TOGETHER

there is NO Risk of getting AIDS!

Become a great cook

just write love letters

give chocol...

play hard to get

board games

you can't catch a...

holding hands

take dancing lessons

Make a fuss dressi...

Staet some mad hobby you always dreamt about

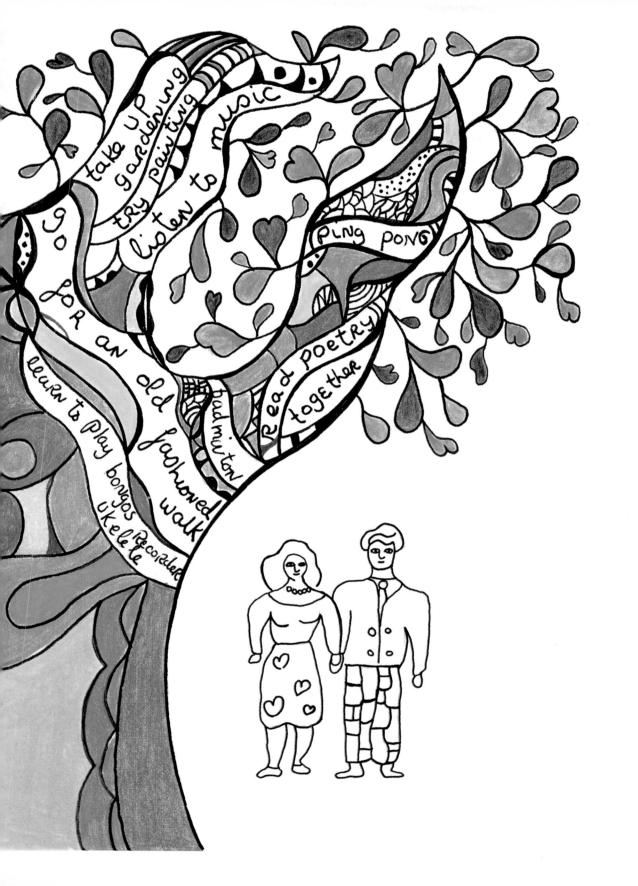

take up gardening
try painting
listen to music
go for an old fashioned walk
learn to play bongos Recorder ukelele
badminton
Read poetry together
ping pong

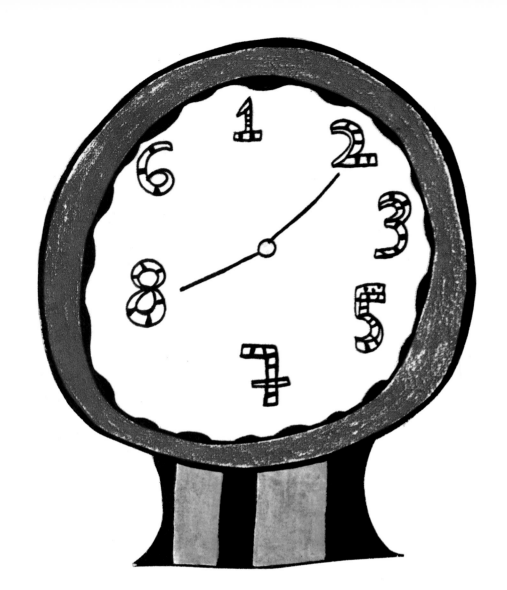

TAKE YOUR TIME
DON'T RUSH anything
(it makes it more exciting!)

BE IMAGINATIVE with your LOVER

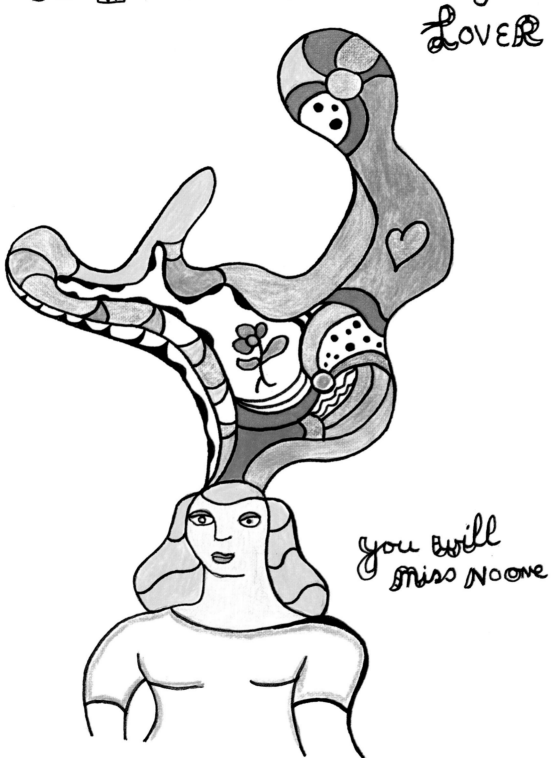

you will miss Noone

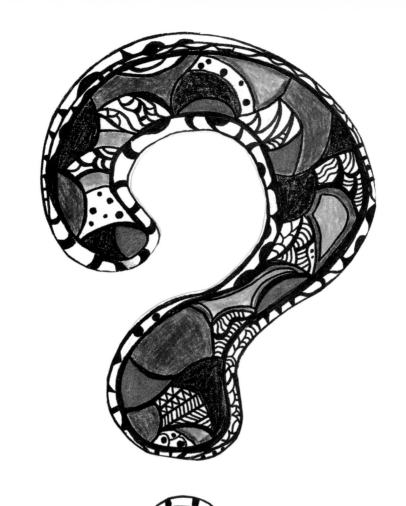

If you have a SERIOUS DOUBT have a test.

If you have a positive blood test. Tell your Lover. Tell your dentist. Tell a doctor who knows about AIDS – OR go to an AIDS center.

If your girl friend has a positive blood test, she should not get pregnant. She can transmit AIDS to her child and to you.

Positive men should not have children because they might transmit AIDS to their wives and babies.

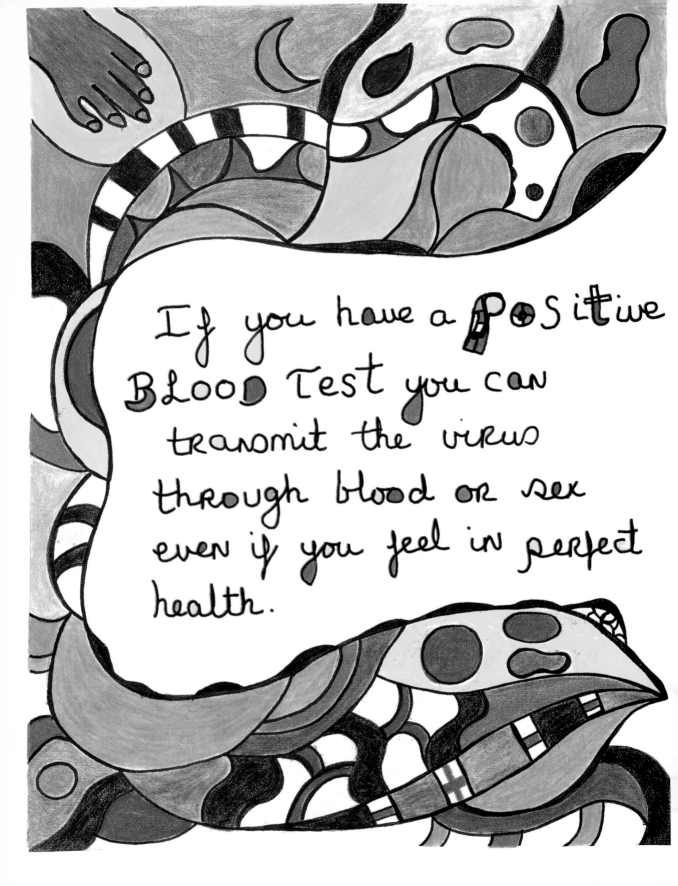

If you have a POSitive Blood Test you can transmit the virus through blood or sex even if you feel in perfect health.

If you have a Positive Blood Test DO NOT Donate BLOOD and protect your partner from direct contact with your BLOOD and SPERM

If your girl friend is Positive protect yourself from her Vaginal fluids.

If you have a positive blood who have infectious diseases. trigger the dormant AIDS

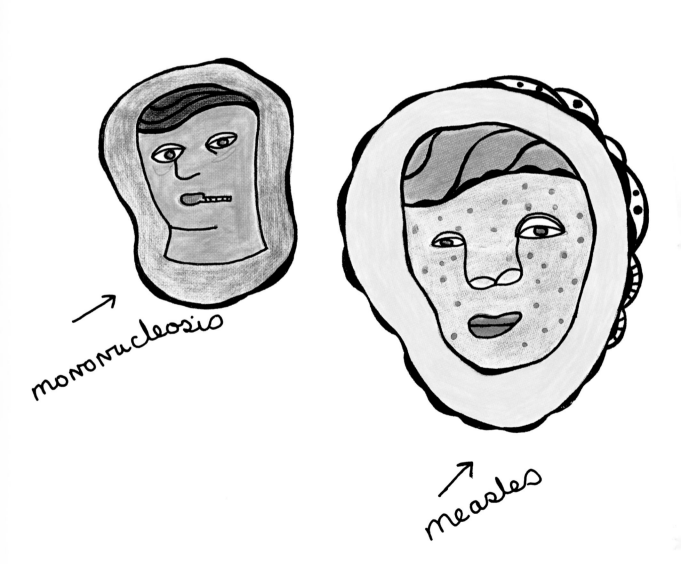

mononucleosis

measles

test avoid contact with people
Repeated infections could
virus.

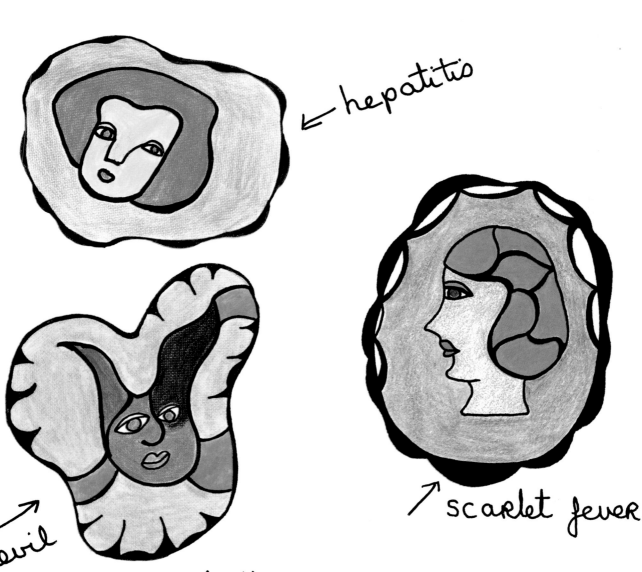

hepatitis

devil

venereal diseases

scarlet fever

There are thousands
of people
DYING
with AIDS
ALONE
because of
IGNORANCE
AND
FEAR

HELP!

The WORST part of all SERious disease is the ANXiety it causes in those who are sick and to those who love them. WE MUST OVERCOME OUR FEAR

WHEN SOMEONE HAS AIDS, IT'S SAFE to be FRIENDLY

laugh with them

cry with them

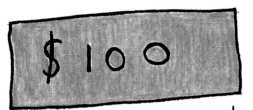

$ 100

If you want to do
something, give money
to AID   FOR AIDS

OR

give your
time
visiting the
stricken.

microscope

PROGRESS is being made through Research. One day this disease will be overcome.

Aids is Everyone's Problem and No One's Fault.

If each one of us takes care and is Responsible Aids will be under control.

Until then we must learn to live with Aids.

Dearest PHILIP,
PLEASE be
careful and let me know
if you have any questions.
Love and Kisses
x   x from
              your x
         x   x
         Mother
                    x